RELIEVED & RELOVED

RELIEVED & RELOVED

Thoughts inked in poems and tales

MOUSEY

Relieved and Reloved
"Thoughts inked in poems and tales"
By: Mousey

ISBN: 978-1-7354562-5-6 (Paperback)

Library of Congress Control Number: 2021907857

Front cover image by Alexandra (Alexas Fotos)
Cover Design and Layout design by Quisqueyana Impressions

To order additional copies of this book, visit QuisqueyanaPress.com or Amazon.com or contact:

QUISQUEYANA
Press

Quisqueyana Press
Poway, California, USA
info@quisqueyanapress.com
www.quisqueyanapress.com

Table of contents

INTRODUCTION

Take a stroll through my mind; tour each cavern filled with emotions and enjoy each ballad filled with quotes, celebrating my happiness, sweat during my misfortune, embrace my soul as my pulse thumps uncontrollably. Weep as my love trails off, losing grips on my sanity over who matters the most, describe my pages in your own words or just imagine…

I have relieved my heart, saved feelings, and circumstanced my love, in order to feel that feeling towards her, I have reloved my special half as she accepts my pride during our brief stay, entertaining each other. This book is the collection of all my poems and tales, not only from my personal life but from the observation of my mind through my eyes of many special people and heart-catching circumstances that surround me.

I've grown to LOVE

Silhouette

The night is darkest just before dawn; my eyes focused on time to witness beauty at its best. Her silhouette glistened as she rolled over onto her back, revealing flawless cheekbones & a perfect pair of lips seemed to pucker effortlessly, glistening somehow through the shadows. Sensing my presence, a tiny smirk curves those lips. Her essence finds its way around this room, softening the shaded areas while coating my lens with a substance unknown to most, causing my irises to dilate the more I fantasized about an endless future by her side. Opening her big, sexy eyes simultaneously with the first rays peeking through the shades, widening her smile as she feels my hand caress her lobe. She stares directly at me, sighing before asking me how my dream ended up after she left...

Praise

He sings nothing but praise from his heart, sings about his tumultuous life, nothing else matters to him at this present time, but he studies this path created from his mind. Praise & glory follows this ultimate journey he's prepared for. From the breaths he's taken, the world has been the audience he searched for. His focus remained undeterred, heart pumping life vigorously throughout his body while he.... sings of glory, acknowledging his achievements based on his direction. About the future his mind created by undying determination, he carries on. His inspired skills were a trademark considered priceless. Tumultuous behavior stifled his minds' focus, so he subtracted... Life goes on from the happiness displayed through his vocal cords. Nothing mattered to him this much as he clears his throat for an encore.

Friendzone??

She's my ace, my ride or dies, my heartbeat. She hugs my mind when I enter my stresses, she gives me a reason to go righteous, accepts my upbringing, respects my life. She knows how I love my other half as she taught my love to embrace it. She's everything to my world a friend should be let alone my thoughts of a connection between our hearts. She's beautiful; perfect in any aspect, smarter than the average, filled with an emptiness only her future lover can endure, filling it with his heart's work as she marvels at his introduction into her story. How can this be possible if I alone know this? Dare I reveal my truth to her & risk my loss as the trustworthy love for her grows into a lust to love her as my better half? I think she knows; glancing at my shirt which seems to move as my heartbeats thump louder than ever as she approaches my peripheral & kisses my lips to my astonishment before undressing my thoughts & laying hers before my naked eyes...

Casualties

She tried her best to hold onto his heart, feeling the love drift away from her grasp as she searched for another excuse to belong in his life. She tried her best to rekindle what she destroyed, not realizing how much he suffered by her doing. She tried her best to explain her mistake, trying to goad him into accepting this false hope of security. She tried her best to show him how much he meant to her by caressing his lobe... Whispering his name, asking him to remember the way he adored when she kissed his ear after biting it gently.... she tried everything she could, knowing that the casualty dealt was by the hands of a soul scathed...

Answers needed

I f love is a feeling, could it be shared? Can it be shared among two people? How would it be divided equally if one cannot identify portions? How much is needed to solidify a soulmate? What if it wasn't relinquished by the same person who abused it? What governing methods would one consider when applying this emotion to a relationship? Can this be upheld during a turbulent chapter in ones' life? Is it really heartfelt if a person professes their true feelings despite no reciprocation?

Apologies

I've opened the hurt, acknowledged the wrong on my behalf, losing that which is most precious to me. Deeply saddened, I'm adjusting my heart to accommodate the pain coursing throughout my life. I longed to watch her eyes light up my peripheral as I approached her perfected stance. I now stare at her departure, grimacing from the pain dealt by my own selfishness. She deserves more than my worth; I dare not stand in her path, stifling her growth for meager reasons pertaining to my pride...

A full mind

I woke up with love on my mind, smelling her sweet scent still floating in the air as if she just walked out. Smiling at her portrait on my phone as it rings. Answering only hear this goddess speak heavenly quotations into the atmosphere as I close my eyes. Drifting towards paradise, hearing nothing but pleasantries from her lungs which seemed to breathe energy & love my direction. I could imagine her pretty face smiling & blowing kisses at me, telling me she adores so much. I would respond & tell her how much she means to me as she giggles in delight. Yes, she shows an equal amount of love which is displayed in her demeanor whenever my name is mentioned or thought of. Gratitude worn beside her pride while she handles my heart with care. She gives more than enough love to last a lifetime. Yet, I always wake up yearning for a little more. I'm spoiled.

A new jacket

My jacket fits a little snug; she helped fasten the straps with her eyes... crossing my arms, simultaneously helping my dilemma. She kisses my lips with her mind, tickling my lust as I find myself following her every wish. Her image seems to be etched under my eyelids; finding a way to ease this feeling is a direction known to few... reaching out to her heart; grabbing her arm, smiling as she comes closer to my life. Unable to see her as I realize I'm holding myself, falling over the chair where she first greeted me, I know now this jacket was designed to love the only one that matters...

You've held my love at bay

Gathering remnants of my soul before enticing my mind with a smile as you danced from within the creases of my imagination, feeding my peripheral unbeknownst of my will to adore the only goddess to secure her mortal...

Nonchalant

Her calm relaxes the atmosphere she inhabits; people smile after noticing the serene created while the mood brightens up, opening up fists of anger to hold on to the love distributed throughout the environment in her attendance. She's alone, yet accompanied by stress-bearers & saddened individuals seeking relaxation from strenuous activities of daily rituals, dragging their poor souls through bottomless ponds of mud...everything mellows out with each step she takes towards the epicenter...

Seasons

My love has frozen during my first lonely winter without her. Unable to blanket my heart as the snow did the earth, sending chills throughout my body. She reappeared suddenly, bringing me close to her bosom which warmed my insides. I felt her heartbeat entirely, causing me to love spring as much as I loved her. She thawed my heart with her love as the days went by... Our lovemaking sizzled up during a late summer rendezvous, bringing my blood to a boil from her smooth touch. Cooling her jets off afterward causing me to fall back in the autumn, her smile brought color beyond my dimples, as we watched the brightened leaves hit the ground. Feeling nippy as the moisture froze in the air forming flakes, she covered my heart with her soul.

Obsessed dreamer

I thought of you ever since I've laid eyes on you. I thought of what it would be like if I married you, I thought of waking up next to you, I thought you'd be ok with my thoughts, I thought I was the man in your dreams......I used to think that until I've realized that your heart pumps my blood through it...now I'm the man in your reality...

What once was

She was my better half; she accented the curve on my smile, activated my joy with kisses, slowed my heartbeat with her caressing & tender touches... She was a great person to befriend, a perfect host to listen to my heartfelt emotions as they spilled in her path. I respected her as my woman. She maintained my heart from her whereabouts, giving me the feeling of completeness whenever she comes to mind... that bond has never been broken, despite the distance or status... I've held a place in my heart to accommodate her thoughts & feelings as she has done mine, what once was will continue for the rest of my life.

Your truth

I thought about what you would mean to the man in your life, what you would mean to your peers, what you would mean to your family, what you would mean to your neighborhood, what you would mean to your coworkers, what you would mean to the next person to walk into your life, what you would mean to the bartender pouring your next drink, what you would mean to that group of men glaring at your person while you walk pass them, what you would mean to the women in the salon you frequent, making you a priceless thought?

I love you

I loved you from the day the earth stood still; I love you unequivocally as I orbited the sun. I will love you as the season changes. I love how you frown whenever I walk away from you. I also love the way you smile in my presence. I love watching you search my belongings for a place to belong. I still love admiring your exit with my property as you sashay those sexy hips in front of my wandering focus. I love how you despise other women's admirers when they announce themselves in my presence. I love your reaction as I reach for your heart still as they scowl in embarrassment. I love how you remember II worship your love. I love how we synced for future references... I love you.

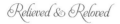

Your soul

Your soul contains your beauty in its purest form & displays it for the world to admire, sometimes stripping men of their courage to approach you. Your smile creates a euphoria know to the few claiming to have loved you in their illustrious past. Your curve brings a distracted response from onlookers concentrating on your tumultuous stride as the perfection completes its final journey towards the apex. You are beautiful, bearing flaws of insecurity secreted through the pores above your heart. You deserve only the determined, the courageous, or the majestic in order for your lives to entwine while hosting each other's lives. By then will your heart play host to his advances, blocking out negativity if there need be.

Woman

The strongest word in any vocabulary. It gives the man insight into what it means to be superior in all aspects of life. Having the ability to show emotion in certain instances, embracing his faults as an inheritance, taking time off her already busy schedule to accommodate his tumultuous life & feed his soul with sweet nothings as if to raise his confidence... Enriching her surroundings with pure energy & love, infecting any & everyone she comes into contact with, leaving inspirational perfection in her wake.

Smile

I love your smile; it carries me extra days when I don't feel like doing a thing, it caresses my shoulders after removing the world from it, I greet your hold on my heart openly, I feel your thumbs massaging my atriums while your fingers seduce my ventricles... I smile back, giving you a reason to keep your soul filled with my happiness.

Tears

She has an uncanny talent: I can't explain how it's so fluent when she does this... At times I think it's a falsity, then the reality becomes my sight. Too weak to stop her overbearing pressure, prying open my ducts with her words, watching me cry uncontrollably as she contemplates my love... my face hardened from the dried-up tears, unable to talk straight ...stripped of my confidence, finding myself at her mercy.

Never change

I've held you in my heart ever since I've laid eyes on you. That will never change. My prayers for your future will never change. My love for you will never change. My respect for you will never you will never change...I've accepted you into my life as a friend; don't feel like an outsider...if I can do anything within my power to help better your life, let me know...this is from my heart...you'll always have a true friend over here...

Mindset

She glared at her competition; she cried for acceptance, she worried about her future. She wondered while attempting the impossible, she wished for a better life, she focused on her true goals, she committed to his love & direction, she sighed in his arms as she planned to excel in her studies, she expected congratulatory behavior from her peers, she celebrated her self-produced achievements, she loved the warm reception from the world, she acknowledged the foundation that mentored her, she rejoiced among family, she frowned at the envious few in the shadows, she disagreed with their faults, she assumed they were neglected individuals in search of a real sense of belonging, she congratulated her supporting peers who never left her side, often shielding her from the hatred spewed in her direction, desperate to inflict harm on her mindset. She smiled, looking back at the adversity which seemed to crumble in her wake...

Pep talk

I'm your man; I know I'm not what you accustomed to, but I belong to you. You have inspired me to go out & get what I've always wanted: I only want you. It may sound like a load of crap, but since we've been talking, I've been one of the happiest dudes in Queens... it's like someone lifted the boulder on my back & gave me freedom to be happy... that person also placed her love into my pores, giving me that full of love feeling all day ...this man will love you till the end of time. He will make love to you for the rest of your life. He is going to be in your face until he falls asleep, preferably on you or behind you, maybe underneath as well.... his heart beats for one person only, & she knows it. Maybe she wants to act naive & be happy when he surrounds her with gifts & chocolates, as well as family outings & get-togethers. He's well on his way to heaven; all he's waiting on is her hands, so he won't get lost.... he loves his angel to the fullest of his heart.... his soul is protected by her halo wings. She understands his need for her acceptance, so she accommodates all of his feelings. She listens whole-heartedly to his poetry as well as the letters of love written with her love on his mind...

Windows

I looked into her eyes, in search of her soul. I studied her irises as they dilated, showing darkness from its absence. Blinking repeatedly as they placed a look of attendance & focused her pupils onto the target intended. She said that her eyes saw real beauty & it mirrored her entire being. I agreed, squinting towards her smile as her soul strafed past my line of sight. Looking beyond the color of her lens somehow brightened, I was able to pinpoint the opening to her soul. It swirled behind her cornea, taking up space in both eyes as they stared back into mine. I must've invited her soul to coexist alongside mine, feeling a slight movement behind my cornea. Judging from her excitement, my acceptance garnered happiness from her lips as they kissed mine lovingly.

Soul

You float in my mind ever so often, blowing me a kiss as you drift by. I sometimes follow your lead, hoping for a chance of a lifetime. Noticing Your presence inspires me to achieve future goals, raising my standards to new heights...I sometimes feel your aura pushing me towards perfection, allowing me to find the path suited for a leader. A soft kiss on my frontal lobe as you vanish with the mild breeze assures the obvious; thank you for occupying the emptiness in my life...

Traveler

I've traveled this winding road all my life, adding love & special people along the way; my heart carried & shared between the hatred & envious, igniting their passions to pursue realism from the shadows whence they stood, too afraid to lead for fear of losing their way or getting trampled... I've swallowed my pride, watching the superficial cross paths of the meek without any repercussions or assistance towards their goals. I followed the overbearing, witnessed pure conceit from their shallow pride, laughed as they were outcasted by their own for failure to adhere to selfish guidelines. I loved the scenery to my left, filled with happiness as bright as the sun which wrapped up its day, united patiently waiting on his lunar friend to relieve this shift divided between them. Losing my step as I gaze at the stars in the distant horizon, focusing on the brightest one while seated on a bed of lilacs.

Weakened Support

Shoulders built to withstand weights of frustrated peers; yet unable to support his own. Where can he lean; how can he handle the problems surrounding his tumultuous life while being the great friend he's always been? Who will embrace his strife as his days remain shrouded in negativity?

Uphill

Treacherously steep, covered with debris, my destiny awaited. Amid pitfalls & jagged rocks, I trekked, searching for any reason to belong. Stones were loosed every other step, creating a path chosen only by judgment... Quietly strafing past a pair of boulders to find myself on a short stretch of cobblestones, followed by a dirt trail filled with remnants of my life. The close I got to the top, the muddier my life felt as my feet seemed to sink with each step into the future.

Thankful

Thank you; I smiled at you because of your beautiful nature. I walked with you, allowing me to express my mind, somehow fumbling my diction. I thought of a life passing me by if we never made contact. You kissed my mind, opening pores in my brain, revealing your inner beauty as well. I now have & will pride myself on having walked with a superior being. A person able to realign your thoughts & include themselves as they're being processed.

Significant

This man before you know how to love his woman, how to cherish her, how to respect her, how to enjoy his days by her side, how to make her life heavenly... you'll learn him, then love him as he will his woman... you know where his heart is; feeling that extra pulse shouldn't make you nervous, he's just as excited as you are to make room for his love. He feels his heart reaching out to you... He hears your pulse inviting his soul; He sees your love becoming one with his, knowing your spirit will be catered to as his significant other...

Pureness

Imperfections should not outweigh judgment, while acceptance displays genuine character... Letting love go should guarantee a safe return, if patience allows such motions to flourish among outsiders... inconsistencies will not be tolerated near truths, forcing realism into the atmosphere among counterfeits creating an honest environment...

Passionate takeover

This woman walked into my life, took up residence in my mind, rearranged my heart & placing hers beside mine. Marking her territory as she appeared in my thoughts the very first time, her thirst for love led me to believe we were destined to be the greatest union ever known. She is my woman; from her gorgeous locks tithe the prettiest smile ever known to man. The softest hands holding my heart in place, synced with her thoughts as a never-ending display of togetherness maintains the smile she displays. Subtracting all of my issues as I welcomed her commitments to my heart.

Needless wants

She wants a great man, not noticing the one pursuing her as she screens for perfection. She searches high & low for that reality expected as her life-mate, shooting down advances from averages as he fades away from her peripheral.... he walks past as she scrutinizes trendy vehicles, looking for securement from naysayers & liar; expecting fulfillment from such people, not even noticing a happier woman dancing about besides her with a familiar person, shaking his head while she suddenly remembers why his face rings a bell....

Revisited & cherishable

I met her in Paris; I loved her in New York. I cherished her in Ontario, I dined her in Sweden...she returned the favor in China, we danced in Greece, made love in Berlin, held each other in Great Britain, followed each other's hearts in Egypt, circled our souls in Australia... Our love maintained a steady heartbeat while floating in Venice, I noticed her smile widen as we strolled the great wall of China, lavishing her with jewels from the Nile ...she stopped me, placed her hand over my lips as she locked her bedroom eyes with mine, toasting our future by the candlelight overlooking Niagara Falls. I asked her to love me forever she asked me to remove her hurt as we trekked across Moscow to appreciate the way she leaned on my heart during a break in Pisa, entertaining my humor watching a geisha fanning herself as she complimented our union in the middle of Tokyo, romanced the duration of our weekend together in Rio de Janeiro, enjoyed the sounds of peace cruising on the cobblestone streets of Rome... waking up from light kisses on my lips from Paris, she's my permanent trip in romance...

My one true love

She admired me from a distance, hoping to replace my wandering lust with genuine love. She coveted my heart as I stared into her eyes, but never meeting them.

I held her close to me as I flirted with stains of insecurity, kissing her soul with my lips, soiled by my greed. I loved her, desired her, used her without reciprocation towards what would bring remorse to my heart as she released her hold on what she thought was solely hers. I look back at the damaged road I chose, wishing my choice to be by her side again to come to fruition. As my eyes met hers for the first time ever, I understood her love to be immortalized among the angelic beings capable of returning such emotions...

Prayers' love

I look to the skies, turning my thoughts into words as my eyes scanned the clouds waiting for answers to appear... My fingers tightly interlocked around each other, letting out a whisper to myself before raising my decibels for passersby to listen in if they chose to do so... I asked for true love to find me, I wanted to feel my significant others grasp on my heart... I wanted her to understand my place in her life, I wanted her to accept me unscathed, filled with happiness by her doing. I ask that you bless me with an angel possessing all of these abilities, entitling me to reciprocate all of her love as she locks both hands around my heart... AMEN

Searching

I need love; I yearn to feel that rush of happiness when she kisses my lips. The warmth of her touch melting my loneliness, overflowing the emptiness in my heart with her sweetness. Embracing my faults while I tearfully accept her role as my better half, no longer hemorrhaging throughout my soul from being hurt, I'll smile whenever she attends my peripheral. I'll celebrate whenever she crosses my mind, surrounding the atmosphere with her beautiful aura. I've looked all over, experienced the feeble-minded, saw true love dashed aside for materialistic objects... instead, I want to own this feeling, searching near & far, high & low... nothing insight; I'll wait until she appears. Soon, I hope...

My dearest

Thank you once again for teaching my heart to see true beauty... you are beautiful. A gorgeous chocolate smile to accent those precious eyes. Broad shoulders & back, assisting those piercings to stand at attention when you greeted the world...Curves aligned with the surface of the heavens allowing your majestic stride to strafe past the mediocre with each step. You should know now, I took a leap of faith because I fell head over heels for someone, I believed entered my life to love me when in fact she appeared only to bring unconditional love into my heart, encased by her will to improve my I am loving, period... I was fortunate to have been your man for a short time, so I took the advantage of living beside an angel seriously. I need you to smile.

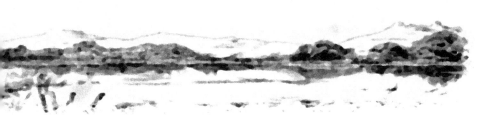

smile when you're alone, smile when you see your kids, smile when you hear your dad, smile when you're at work, smile around your haters, smile when you feel your soul leave your body to compliment mine distances away. You're a goddess in my world. All I had to offer was my heart, you had your heart, your kids, your soul, your smile, your superstar persona, your heels & beauty. Don't worry about me; I'm thousands of miles away, dreaming of you, knowing that you're beautiful in every aspect & believing you can stand up & walk over any hill stifling your progress & clinging to your already battered heart. I just wish I could love you as your mate, holding you in your hour of need, kissing your smile after greeting your curves which accents that proud posture of a completed Queen. If only I could caress that strong cheekbone as you smiled before me once more... I love you.

Yours truly,

Memory

Igniting her soul with my lips; whispering sparks of love that flows through her veins, sending a slightly chilled message into her heart. She feels my pulse, she smiles at my demeanor, she holds my attention exclusively... I gazed into her eyes, noticing the dilation as she sighed with the touch of my hands. Flickering her lovely lashes, puckering those soft lips to kiss my dimple after telling me how I made her fall in love with me all over again...

Just thought of her

Writing a few thoughts about that special woman whose been on my mind, but unable to see me due to her importance to the world. I will hold her heart next to mine until she decides to entertain my thoughts about a perfect love in her soul. I will think about how she compliments me while I await her arrival into my life as my better half. I will celebrate her love so the world will come to understand the depths of our bond. She will adopt my values as my better half, showing our happiness through her smile. We will admire onlookers as they send us anniversary wishes during the lifetime, we will share caressing each other's soul...

She

She nourished my battered heart with a love unknown to most; she cleaned the wounds which impaired my ability to love another woman. She talked to me as if I was by her side forever, adoring the soft smile portrayed after kissing me. She wiped the tears of pain from my eyes while caressing my mind with uplifting words of gratitude. She embraced my flaws as if they accented her aura, glowing simultaneously with her being. She told me to stand tall, regardless of my checkered past as she feels for my faint pulse. She warmed my bosom with hers, jumpstarting my love to embrace her doing as her lashes invited my soul to coexist. She loves me, for as long as she could recall, admiring my dimples as they'd sink in her presence. She secured only the place vacated by the meek, contributing her love to the foundation left for her to cherish for all eternity. She deserves every accolade, every kiss, every hug, every rose gifted by my hands. I thank her every chance I get, rewarding her smile with one of my own.

His guardian angel

He thinks of his angel often, wondering what's on her mind. At times he could feel a light breeze as she flutters her wings overhead, guarding her mate...yes, he loves her unequivocally as she loves him... She knows his hearts' location; actually, it's in her possession...she keeps it safe from all others determined to disrupt the flow of happiness they share.

Her greatness

She's good to me; she kisses me every day, she reminds me of her love. She brings so much positive energy into my life; she gives me the smile only deserving of an emperor. She knows when to correct my mistakes, she cheers me on whenever I challenge myself, she helps me shed my coat filled with hatred. She knows my thoughts, making it impossible to surprise her with gifts from my heart, she protects my feelings from envious beings bent on disrupting the flow created by our union, she appreciates my dedication as much as I do hers. She keeps me grounded with her realism; she knows how to cherish her man. She loves when I hold her tight & secure her heart; she's good to me.

Friend

Friend: how does one earn that title? Making time to show support from the heart, bringing honesty to any conversation...always present amidst your strife, providing love throughout pain riddled circumstances...putting their life on hold just to comfort a friend in need...that title goes to the unique, truthful individual that matters...thanks, friend.

Me

This is your life; you need not worry about the fingers pointed at you, laughter cushioning your every step...pay close attention to the only person who's never left your side, shielding your ears from sharp insults. Look at me; those mild jokes shouldn't distract your focus... Jealousy desires to fit your shoes, hatred needs to consume your positivity, meanwhile, I'm still defending you & keeping you focused.... just follow my lead, it seems easier...

Existence

What if I wasn't born? What if I never loved? What if I couldn't feel? What if I didn't matter? What if I lost that which was most precious to me? What if I was denied a choice? What if I refused my purpose? What if I hated my existence? What if I never knew a single being known to most as a friend? What if I smiled at passerby instead of this horrid scowl I employ as a greeting tactic? What if I lived among my peers, silenced by their griefs? What if I felt remorse towards jealous rivals, targeting my successful stride? What if I was aborted, unable to cry as I exited her womb? What if I couldn't celebrate, barred by my own selfishness? What if I ran out of thoughts to continue this mindless banter...what if...?

Missing my past

Dilated people confused my history; interrupting my stride as I come to grips with a false reality. Staging themselves in order to disable my focus one step at a time during a brief stay in my peripheral in which we coexisted before II blinked repeatedly as if to sweep away particles nearing my corneas. I've digested their lies, inhaled envious intentions, listened with the pureness I've kept guarded besides my judgment my entire life. Traitors created by the sun during its progression over the advances in my life leading me towards my demise before losing way once it sets behind my every step from this future, I've created by my focused aim...

Chanced

Her choice reflected perfection, admiring him from afar, evenly appreciating his brown eyes, handsome smile as well as his softened demeanor. Her will to be loved followed by his hearts' desire for acceptance superseded all other emotions during their first encounter. Their bond became inseparable throughout the years as she massaged his soul with drops of her love, deepening his dimples. He'd already donated a smile alongside the love promised, holding her trust at bay while entertaining their future values alongside his battered heart.

Complacently

I fall short of my goals all of the time; Spending lots of time in the lobby behind my eyes, mostly sharing arguments with my new tenant who seems to be there taking up refuge from progress. For some reason, feel a dependency towards this being no matter what. He makes me feel nervous around success & happiness, clouding my determination with uncertainties, raising my insecurities & shallow feelings towards completion. I've been offered excuses from his gift bags, exclusive but nonexistent reasons to cancel future endeavors. I find myself following footprints, seemingly leading me back to where I started...

Dilated love

Counting her blessings as my own; coating the very heart, which was consumed by my love, she hears but a whisper from my lips, experiencing eternal bliss...watching her pupils dilate the closer she got to where I stood, hearing the strongest heartbeat pound against the cavity before her certified my place in her life. Controlling my smiles with a touch of her spice, enjoying the freshness of this newfound love as I strolled carelessly among peers... Witnessing sadness from the lonely-hearted searching for what I was gifted...

Distance

Does love have boundaries? Can one be separated from her feelings due to the barrier created from distance? Can love to supersede not being able to caress her body? Kiss her lips as she would want? Whispering into her ear while she melts into your arm? Telling her that you belong to her... Can you strengthen your heart, making you a prime candidate to share your life with her? Love gives out these instances, accepting the courageous & overlooking weaker beings unable to sustain true emotions because of absence only in the mind & soul...

Distracted

She said my name; I've always wanted her to notice my admiration for her. She looks my way ever so often, smirking before turning away. Even dropping her keys wondering if I would look over at her & check her out, only to find me before her, catching the keys as they near the ground. Thinking about her all the time makes me smile, revealing dimples while my eyes become narrow slits. I want to grab her by the waist & look right into her big, beautiful eyes & tell her how much she means to me. I want her to jump into my arms & kiss me lovingly... she gets up & walks towards me, strutting her sculpted body, only wearing a bra & boy shorts.... she said my name again before taking the remote out of my hand & completing her thoughts in my ear as I freeze with anticipation while she straddles my lap... "Your turn to take out the trash...

Dreamt reality

Inspired by her heart, followed by her desire, trusted with his love, boasted by her confidence to overcome any & all obstacles, she chooses her future wisely. Securing a place in her heart for his occupying love which seems to follow her every step, she longs for his return. Knocking on her door, lifting her spirits with his arrival... she tries to run, falling out of her slumber, finding herself face to face with her slippers...she felt his soul caress her sore body, raising not only her mind but the level of love she felt while he was away...

Relieved & Re-loved

She walked into my life suddenly, following the trail of despair left by my heart... She claimed my soul, she smiles at my pain, evicting emotion from my opened heart while carefully treating it with her own remedy of soothsaying and love quotes. I stared anxiously into those big, brown pupils, wiping the lone tear from my cheek with her thumb as she kissed me. Flickering her lashes, focusing my eyes to see this gorgeous woman grasp both my hands & wrap her petite frame up with them, letting out a sigh...

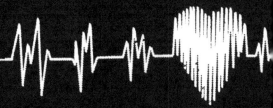

A practiced apathy

pologies towards my behavior while her love displays a longing during his absence. I frowned as her shoulder blades aimed in my direction, loosening as he hugs her once he enters the venue, glancing at my demeanor before displaying his undying love towards her rosy cheeks after kneeling before her anxious stance. Shrugging, I felt my hold on her essence loosen as I took a sip on my way out of her life, possibly for good. I looked at her figure one more time before I disappeared into the shadow of the vestibule ahead of my future. Clearing my head once again, I walked a few steps towards uncertainty as my judgment interacted with my emotions. Forcing my heart into an unfamiliar zone, I paused at the sound of her voice calling my name as I neared the curb. She reached for my hands as my smile disappeared after she handed me the keys I've left as I exited for the last time.

Pauper

His heart boasts unspecified amounts of love towards her, still not able in to express his truth. He makes up for this, following her story until he finds an opening for his life to intervene. Reaching out to her attention to show his intentions, she smiles his direction as he shies away again, dropping his heart this time as she notices it beating to her pace. Picking up the stained & battered organ, she notices the sudden burst of energy as it pumped the color of love vigorously throughout its outer layer. Remembering the direction, he retreated to turning to see the battered & torn body standing to her left...manicured hands touching the filth-riddled shoulder of this man with a homeless heart...wiping the sadness away from the ventricles as she chooses to enrich his life with her fortune...

Emptiness stares

I can feel someone watching me, piercing the serene with their eyes. Looking over my shoulders, I see nothing & hear just as much. I know someone's there, feeling a slight unrest in my stride as I ducked into a vestibule to avoid this trail. Someone's there, keeping a safe distance from my peripheral while haunting my senses. Silhouettes shifting as I step out of hiding, creating new shadows within my sight...whispers become shouts to my right, taps to my left shoulder. Ignoring the sounds across the street, I strolled towards the spotlight which seems to be silent upon my arrival, feeling the eyes of the world screening what they presume to be flawed to my character.

Salvaged

Reading the signs before her eyes distracted her thoughts as she strolled past my person, still warped from a previous encounter. I loved her unconditionally while her heart displayed signs of infidelity. Her selfishness led my eyes away from desires expected by her lust. I covered my soul as she shared hers among the savored; neglecting the very man destined to love her unconditionally, tearing into the cavity before her unfocused eyes as mine shed. Unable to see my future bettering itself to host my heart, feeling ahead for direction...

Suicide

I looked over the ledge, feeling the breeze...I can't go on, I thought. She stripped me of my feelings, I don't want to be here, this room revealed our faults a thousandfold... The cold air causes shivers down my back ... confused about my future, watching her walk towards her future with remnants of my heart in her possession. Taking a leap of faith in hopes of stopping her from making the biggest mistake of her life... the ground stares back as I plunge effortlessly, shouting her name as she drives off, waking up with a serious headache, upside down, drooling on a sealed envelope with my name written on it.

The greatest journey

Conversations with you give me an edge in life. They create visuals as you describe your daily ventures & outings... I would be anticipating a new lesson every time I surround your ears with my weird questions & silly quotes. I wouldn't sound like I'm paying attention, but I'm digesting all of the old lessons as we converse... I learned a lot of stuff from being in your presence; in fact, I am looking into what I could do to better my future besides you as I prepare myself for the greatest journey of my life. I've learned that dreams should be pursued & not just wished on... significant others should be respected, as well as loved unconditionally. I have found my significant queen, will do whatever it takes to secure her, will continue my dedication towards her as the only man in her life.

Melanin

O ur ancestors were once celebrated as superior beings from the tribes they originated. Although they were unable to fathom the hatred spewed in their wake, they searched for one reason to matter towards the heartless individuals promoting this method of alienation when they took them out of their kingdom. Being a proud occupant of this planet & descendants of this prestigious race, their complexions overshadowed the pale green aura surrounding the uneducated & envious minions lacking this spectacular hue which varies accordingly. Acceptance is way beyond their grasp, so long as the daunting task derails what is already instilled within each of them. The darker they appear, the more beautiful. Melanin decorated the very pores of their bodies, making their beauty impervious...

One print

His hands soaked as he clutched his chest; crimson fluid seeps through the cavity, covering his fingers as she claimed his heart no longer mattered. Unable to advance, desperately seeking answers to quell his intuition... his eyes followed the trail left by the sole bloody footprint from where he laid ....ending up exactly where she stood

Mornings

Whispering her name into her ear as I caressed her shoulders...kissing her cheek as her eyes opened, acknowledging my love as it hovered over her essence. Wrapping her arms around my neck & pulling me towards her lips, whispering back sweetness after nibbling on my ear. We rubbed our noses, smiled at each other, she caressed my dimple with three fingers as my smile grew, telling me that she wanted us to last forever. Leaning on her elbow, she sat up partially to place her moistened lips on my neck, gliding her warm tongue around my jugular giving my throat a slick feel, then biting on it lightly; tasting beads of sweat forming as my eyes closed... Feeling both hands holding my shoulders as she kissed my cheek, then my lips .... wishing me a great day as she gets up with a sigh.

Flawless behavior

His complexion attracted her eyes, focusing on his stride while his fragrance surrounded her person... He winked at her, noticing a slight smirk as she turned, blushing... His smile widened, displaying dimples she adored making her sigh heavily.... his shoulders towered over her gentle frame as he excused himself while brushing past her; this time leaning over & whispering into her lobe... followed by a kiss, making her body shiver while she rolled her eyes. The softness of his touch allowed her body to melt into his presence while he ran his fingers across her shoulders, creating a mellow rhythm with her heart...

Honorable demeanor

L isten to me whisper into your soft lobe as your slumber begins; feel my palms caress your lids & cheekbones after I plant a kiss on your forehead... An effortless sleep consumes you; your irises shift as your pupils open up simultaneously while you yawn, signaling your chest cavity to expand a bit more before as you reach for your comfort zone. Your rhythm begins, syncing each heartbeat with your breathing as your pulse supports the exact pace in the background. You smirk, enjoying this procedure as your body contorts comfortably. Letting out a breath of air seemingly as fresh as you inhaled, your lids flickered as you invited my soul to coexist by yours. My fingers grazed over every freckle located on your raised cheekbone, feeling the warmth surrounding you. Your lips invited a kiss from mine as I imagined eternal bliss from the happiness given by choice. I adjusted your pillow, staring at unmatched beauty as your arms reached out as if to hold onto my soul. I safely placed your arms over your heart after I planted a kiss on your wrist. I looked at your lips which seemed to mumble a thankful quote towards my honorable demeanor. Sarcastically smiling as I welcomed your gesture.

Letting go

Guided by his intuition, raised with the best of his knowledge, she learned as much as her mind allowed. He taught her street smarts as well as self-respect throughout high school, allowing her to learn values in life. watching her walk down the aisle to accept her diploma put tears in his eyes... He stood tall & proud to congratulate her accomplishment, gifting her with a kiss on her forehead. Spending his days off with her took up all of his time, knowing that she'll be leaving for college soon... So happy, unable to shake his sadness from watching her walk out the door to pursue her future, he smiles as she kisses his forehead, thanking him for a job like no other... Not wanting to sour a joyous occasion, he covers his sadness reminiscing on the earlier years of parenting; giving her that hug squeezed a lone tear from his eye as she kissed his forehead in honor of a near-perfect job.

Forever & a day

Living alongside her would give my life new meaning. Walking in her shadows could only guarantee my hearts' desire to cloak her essence with my soul. Knowing this, she glides her fingers across my lips, leaving traces of her love accompanied by her smile. Eternity welcomes every step I take towards it, promising her attention at all times while the shadows produced before her irises mimic my every move. She adores my smile; thanking me every day with gestures of sincerity, conversations filled with her gratitude, kisses on my soul surround with the aroma of love. I feel special in her presence, excited at times being introduced as her better half... Waking up beside her would pigment my dreams; looking forward to that moment she accepts my proposal to spend my future alongside the best thing that ever happened to me...

Eviction

I was pursued by her, I was called by her, I responded to her advances as looked into the mirror. I initiated at first, not able to convey my message to her. Finding my love at her mercy, I was ambushed by mixed feelings as she claimed I no longer mattered before requesting a sponsorship towards her future endeavors. I was pursued by her malicious intent to conquer all of my generosity... Pausing briefly to reassure my heart of her evil-doing, I removed her hands from my pocket & seized all that she acquired over time from falsifying love tactics to gain my trust... Evicting her sticky hands from my life as my irregular heartbeat went back to its original state, pumping love throughout my tired & used body...

Forgiveness

Sorrow filled the room as he sobbed at her knees; Refusing his pleas as her anger lingered, staffing past his outstretched arms & grabbing her bag, glancing in his direction briefly before picking up the keys. Ignoring the wails of mercy as she entered the hallway with a stoic look, mumbling to herself about his need to think solely of himself...

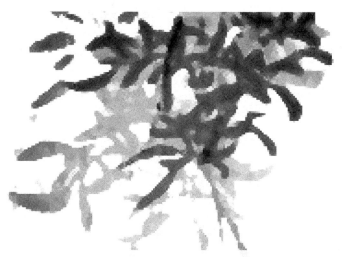

She who hasn't claimed my heart since she whispered into my thoughts as I listened relentlessly for her to make a way for me to host the very love, I have waited for...

Choice

There's only one woman for me in this lifetime; she knows it. She doesn't have to announce that she knows, as long as she knows. My past choices are not mistaking, just lessons in my life about different women. My feelings about having a certain amount of women decreased as I aged gracefully, ending up with that special one woman or queen which I adore whole-heartedly. She loves me as if I conquered nations at her desire, showering her with vast amounts of treasure... she doesn't need these things, as long as her significant other stays by her side...

Between hearts

She loves him, she liked the other; she kissed his lips while giving him a peck on the cheek, she professed her undying love to him, but keeping him within arm's reach, saying yes to his proposal, slowing his advances, getting swept off her feet at dinner while going dutch on his lunch invitation, loving the jewels from his gift-giving, refusing bracelets of courtship, sleeping over at his place, checking the mail at their new home...wearing his polo around the house, displaying the ring he gave her as his future wife, watching sports while she sighs irritably, holding her close while she explains the reality show they're enjoying, impatiently waiting on her to bring his meal, cooking for her after taking her shoes off & rubbing her feet after serving her like a queen should be treated, kissing her before rolling over & sleeping, making sure she's comfortable & kissing her goodnight, going to bed holding her in his arms...

Best dressed

Dressing himself for her eyes, arranging several thoughts aimed at her ears. He tucks his pride in with his shirt, honed only by his will to display his undying love towards her needful soul... He slides the loafers on, smiling at his silhouette as he stands up, towering before her eyes. He feels her eyes, approving the definition from his shoulders to the sharp creases on his slacks. Pushing the cuff links through the eyelets, reaching for his wallet & watch... Pausing just to look into her eyes & blow a kiss. Catching her smile in return, grabbing his jacket before leaning over the bed to place a kiss over her softened lips. She shivers at his touch, prompting him to caress her lobe with his hand before tracing her features lightly.... he thanks her for gracing his life; she thanks him for allowing her to open up his heart as he exits the room...

Awakened

Dormant thoughts aroused by her fragrance: Ambrosia hovering above his senses following the awestruck behavior he displayed as she strolled past his peripheral. Glancing at the smile being fed in her direction, she pauses to adjust her scarf...looking around, acknowledging his attention with a kiss blown through the breeze as their heartbeats synchronized with every breath taken from that moment... Pupils partially dilated from the glare accompanying her every step; nervousness erupts as she reaches for his heart, feeling the warmth from her soul, he relaxes...

A prelude to remember

I kissed you; I took that look of astonishment followed by that gorgeous smile as my reward for requesting your heart by my side. Blushing as you nodded, giving me the answer, I waited for what seemed to be an eternity, I rejoiced, caressing your shoulder gently & lifting your chin to place my lips onto yours. You closed your eyes, relaxing your body as soon as I wrapped my love around you. Your knees buckled, prompting you to fall into my arms as if you planned it. Rubbing your soft, supple skin against my beard created a euphoric response, sending waves of excitement throughout your body you opened your eyes, pupils fully dilated beneath those heavenly lashes, flickering uncontrollably at me...you grasped my forearm as it held your body in place. Grabbing my ears with both hands, you kissed me as you pulled me closer...

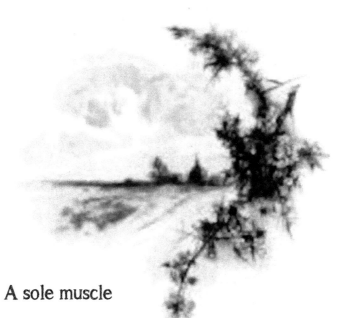

A sole muscle

She smiles down on you; all of whom has been celebrated in her presence, she holds you in her heart still, love carries her soul into your essence, she lives in your actions being inspired by her aura, bringing your heart to beat-heavy, only because her heart beats alongside yours, she's still here, resembling the gift to your friends, you will see her again, you will smile with her again, her smile is yours, hold on to it...

My eyes

Covered with a green tint which shields my senses from the savory. Eyes distracted from the truth as I've been targeted for as long as I can remember. Covered by my intuition to focus on a stride created by progression from my heart. With my pride, I march onward despite holes in my heart from escaped love laced with sour intentions. A second later, the world adjusts to my definition a step into judgment as my cornea scans my peripheral for the imperfected. Green shading seems to loom with every step back into my sight with the sunset. Tint introduces itself, camouflaged as the envious relax beneath the shadows of conspiracy. Which thought should I manufacture as my vision grows sharper amid this reaction from this hate generated from unknown rivalries? Shields from said persons dodge my attendance as to continue their tirades amongst the fickle-minded. My life seems to matter more than their own. Senses already dulled during these encounters I've withstood filled with confusion or questionable authorizations alleged from friends. From my position on this planet, I observed faultiness continuing amid stress-ridden peers in search of guidance. The focus on my story will matter too seriously strategized servants of loyalty. Savory-filled hearts shall not remain before as I love only the unpoisoned or those who've unequivocally accepted my reality...

Her smile

I've noticed her smile in the reflection of my mind; her beautiful eyes kept my attention at bay while she decorated my life once she appeared by my side. Her trimmed locks curled to my liking, coexisting along with my dilated pupils focused on our future after she blew a kiss, resonating for some time after she introduced herself as my better half. We made our love mesh without malice when we held each other, synced to each other's pulse during the first time she placed her softened lips against mine & welcomed me home. She touched my beard, marveling at my lashes before wrapping her warm arms around my life & sighing as she ran both hands through my beard. I began to see her essence somehow drift towards me, glowing a bright auburn hue just before she grabbed my hands. Putting my hands over her cheeks, I watched her become my future while I agreed to love her no matter what as we wiped the lone tear, we both shed simultaneously.

Recognized by my dreams

She winked at my crown as I scribbled every detail on tattered stationery at the corner of my mind as her silhouette reaches out to console the actual actions displayed in her shadow. Admired by my penmanship, she blushed as I fell in love immediately during our very first encounter which plays in my mind over & over. Seeing my pulse erupt as I wished for her to accept my flaws as much as she was perfect towards my esteem, I whispered a tearful plea which caused a chain reaction in my fantasy. Her hand caressed my shoulder unbeknownst to my tuition as she whispered in return, placing her palm onto my chest plate slowing my heart just a tad right before reminding me to cherish what she gave me before exiting minutes ago as the actual knock on my door brought my life full circle, filling my intuition with the scent of lilacs when I opened my mind to her entrance of my eternity...

Drunk

taggering backward after their lips parted, he catches his balance. Biting her bottom lip while staring at his physic which towered over her, marveling at his clumsiness as he took a deep breath left, eyes never leaving hers. A bit groggy from the kiss they shared, he shook his head. Unbelievingly sweet, her aroma seeped into his mind through his nostrils, bringing the impression of her royalty full circle. Focusing on her lips, reaching for her hands, he stands upright to help himself to another kiss... Blissful signals running through his mind as they joined lips, confusing his mind with feelings of euphoria & mild pain as she loses her footing, digging her nails into his arms...This feeling is shared between their souls while in each other's presence or separated... Not wanting to sober up from this state, they engulf all of the love displayed from their hearts....being each other's balance, they return to the kiss that started the intoxicating dilemma...

Pride

I could see your pride from a mile away; bragging to yourself about your fourth comings to where you've placed your soul as your children focused on their destinies. I could picture your smile almost identical to mine as our dimples coexisted on the only photograph, I've held in my possession all these years. I could imagine your demeanor once you see my face & attempt to squeeze my dimples, kissing my nose before hugging me. I could wait all eternity for one day with you, telling my whole days' worth as you sat before me legs crossed. I could expect to hear from your stern voice as the breeze whispered through the open window, brushing past my shoulders. I could understand what you mean to me as I celebrate your touch, your love, your guidance from wherever you stood enabling my choices to be self-taught from your inspiration... I could kiss your soul in spite of your absence, I'd keep your life relevant as I carry on the legacy you helped create. I see you mom... thanks...

My life

Reasoning with my reflection as he begs me not to bring my wallet with me nor my phone. Fearing an onslaught as I conceal both within the folds of my jacket, I argue back as my thoughts reconvene on the curb before their aim, shouting obscenities daring me to draw my weapon of choice which could probably brighten up the shadow of doubt surrounded by their peers as I've been fitted to a description based on a hue gifted to my life...

Accents

He smiles all day, inspiring me to discard my animosities for a second & appreciate life for what it is. He loves all of the strangers in his peripheral as he navigates his seemingly fun-filled life, making his problems fall short of his laughter. He had an accent he used to convey small talk among drinking buddies, loved the smallest things in life, left problems on his doorstep as he entertained in his home. Living his life, the way he wanted, surrounding himself with love & people who cared. His memory will be cherished by his friends & family...

Biological dreams

He's a parent in his mind; yearning for the chance to father any child needing that role. They look up to him in terms of respect, finding his guidance useful.... discipline is hardly ever used, being understood at all angles. She admires his stances on education & future values, never overbearing no matter what problem arises. Those children mean everything to him, sensing their bond into his heart as soon as they were introduced. He's living happier than ever being labeled one of the greatest roles given by those kids. She sees him as a great individual that inspired her children to set higher goals...they've replaced the only non-functioning part of their lives with this genuinely loving, caring, figure who seems to mesh immediately into this daunting task placed into his life as a father...

DEDICATION

Shawnteã; my heartbeat when mine seemed to stop during my strife's; I've thanked the heavens for your introduction into my life, Yoshi; where do I begin with your contribution to my smile. Thank your natural aura as well as your advice which wiped my tears away when I was at my lowest.

First, I would like to thank God who gave me the strength for my life's journey. My mother Raymonde Guerrier rest in paradise, I feel your hands on my shoulders as I write. My father Alfred Jean-Baptiste, you never let me down no matter the circumstances. Raymond, thank you for the world you've created for me to perfect my life before answering his call towards paradise. Princess, you already know my world needs your love and smirks to come full circle with those beautiful children Ray, Imani & Urijah. Dyna & Neheme, your spiritual guidance raised my determination Melvin Coeur with those jokes and nonstop progress reports allowed me to concentrate on certain goals, Nerlande Nelson,

Monisha Williams & lil Makai as Noah staring in my arms accent the rest of my mind and add a little class to my project.

Amanda, Nathaelle, Berniece & Claire Francois, you are my world. I'm thankful for Janel Whytes' inputs and positive conversations giving me unlimited material to align every corner of my mind. Jeff Masse & Lisa Copingon for helping me perfect my craft. Mark Stennet & Leditra Palmer, your positive energy revealed determination which was well needed. James Moore, Dion McCain, Larry Shannon, Manny Kieth, Camelo Ernesto Guerra, Alberto Modesto, Ravi Marwah from Headquarters Barbershop, my respects for your realness and support; you guys are one of a kind. Latoya Campbell, your desire to watch my poetry flourish helped on those days I wasn't inspired. Aneasha & Ashanti, my dedication to you both for choosing to love me the way you do carries my gratitude to newer heights adding more thoughts into my project. Trina Thomas, Alanna Abraham-Sheard, Yolanda Palmer, Sharon Bonner-Webb, Camille Brammer, Keira Weaver, Mathew Threadgill, Dimitri Glen, Davilla Moore I feel your wings as you guard over your loved ones. Antoinette Little, Michelle Miller, Ernestine Purdy, Chantel & Manny Chambers, Takisha Taylor & Juawanna Roberts for a real feel of family and accepting my tumultuous life, I'll never forget you.

Pastor Georgia Christie-Salmon, your short talks keep my ambitions alive. Fatima & Shaquan Williams, Monique Williams, Chelle Moore, Yahve Alcinay Sa k'ap fèt ! Lisa Miller, Sandra Helene Nixon, I'm hugging your heart with both my mind and soul, thank you for your relentless approach into my life.

Lakesha Pope-Stevens, Eboni Browning, Erika Allen, you guys guided me into lanes of perfected bliss. Brandy Kellerman, Narada Watson, Taefa Mills, Brian Miller, Parris Morris, Sandra & Frank Rogers have been great parents to my direction & goals making them awesome role models. Bryan Stephenson a brother to me when I needed one. Kathy Burchell, Cashel Campbell, Letrice Dyer, Sharon (Shay) Jones I got you and grand! Erika Hayes, Tracey Gamble, Wandra Davis, Ariel Rodriguez & Jasmine Vallejo, Jaques Morel, Tishura Dwyer, Michael Restrepo, Towan & Demetrias Hopkins, Les Boadu with your never-ending perspectives. Candice Stevens for answering my calls even when you were busier than I was. Robert Hunter with your self-help techniques. Lanette Charles & Andre Phillips for mental notes. Narada Watson, Nikki D. Simpkins, Cindy Harden & Prudence Sarrazin-Reid, you guys don't know the level of my appreciation for taking time to read and offer suggestions towards my project. Raqueena Strickland, my heart. Gabrielle Duzant, I love your support, and I'd love to extend my condolences to your son Anthony. Simone Duzant for reminding me how much I have to hustle to get what I need in this life. Corey Moses, Kiara Sheperd, Nelson Vargas, Cleon Tabois, Jeff & Ernestine Fitzpatrick, Wendell Hutchinson, Karl Autea & Jill Dimaano, Ron Uy for bringing my focus back to my poetry with regular conversations. Damian & Kyra Mollison, Kyle, Devon & Devin, you guys entertain my stresses. To my oldest sister Yanique and Jean Lacombe and all my beautiful nephews and niece, know that I love you.

I'd like to thank Maria Aduke Alabi for allowing my first project to flourish in ways I've never thought possible along with Nerlande Nelson, one of the greatest sisters ever gifted to my stride. Lastly, Ervin & Jason Peter, I can't find words to express my gratitude or show my appreciation for you guys and all others I've mentioned beforehand... God blesses you all for your support.

Mousey

EDITOR NOTES:
We accept the excessive use of contraction in some of the poems to respect the poet's style and edit the collection without missing the natural rhythm of each poem. The ellipsis in this content is mostly used to show a pause in speech without missing its formality. The paragraph arrangement -one paragraph per poem- is intentional and required by the poet.

Relieved & Reloved

CPSIA information can be obtained
at www.ICGtesting.com
Printed in the USA
BVHW041151070521
606668BV00003B/365